Make it easy,
English
Quick Tests

Age 7-8

Louis Fidge

Test 1 Prefixes

A **prefix** is a group of letters we put **in front** of a word.
Prefixes **change the meaning** of the word.

Choose the prefix un or dis to complete each word.

1. _____pack
2. _____well
3. _____place
4. _____trust
5. _____fair
6. _____happy
7. _____agree
8. _____may

9. _____load
10. _____bolt
11. _____honest
12. _____do
13. _____arm
14. _____charge
15. _____please

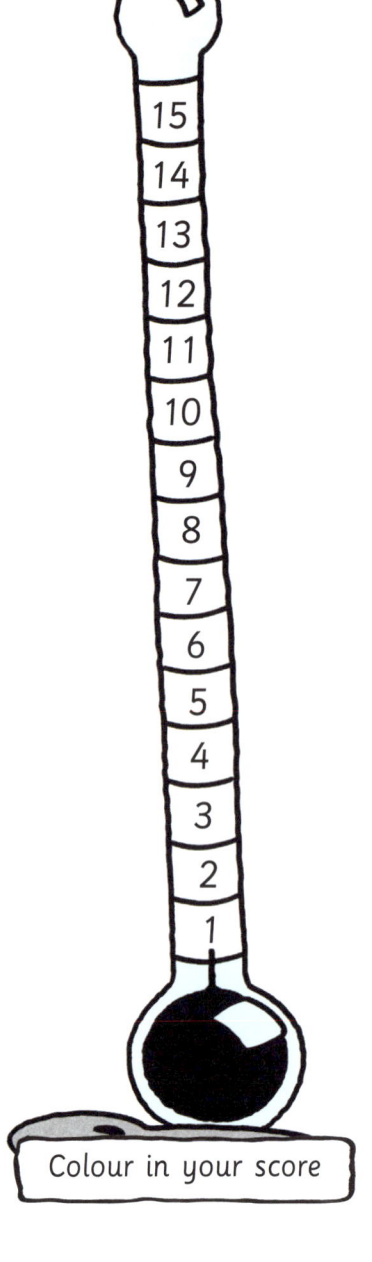

Colour in your score

Test 1

Test 2 Verbs

A **verb** tells us what someone **is doing** or what **is happening**.

Anna **is riding** her bike.

Choose the best verb to complete each sentence.

1. The rabbit _____ into the burrow. (disappeared/spoke)
2. The child _____ in a whisper. (spoke/chased)
3. The bull _____ the boy across the field. (drew/chased)
4. I _____ up all the mess. (brushed/groaned)
5. Abdi _____ a lovely picture. (painted/crashed)
6. Who is _____ at the door? (eating/knocking)
7. The girls were _____ lemonade. (drinking/painting)
8. The injured man _____ with pain. (turned/groaned)
9. The lady was _____ a pram. (raining/pushing)
10. The sun is _____ in the sky. (shining/shouting)
11. A lion _____ loudly. (smiled/roared)
12. The car _____ into the wall. (crashed/crushed)
13. The dragon _____ its wings. (flagged/flapped)
14. The frog _____ onto the log. (hoped/hopped)
15. A letter _____ through the letter box. (came/screamed)

Colour in your score

Test 2

Test 3 Phonemes

A **phoneme** is the **smallest unit of sound**. A phoneme may be made up of **one or more letters** which make **one sound**.

b + oa + t = boat

This word is made by using **three phonemes**.

Choose the correct phoneme to complete each word.

1. m_____n (oo/ir)
2. tr_____t (ee/ea)
3. gr_____ (ow/oo)
4. gl_____ (ue/oo)
5. r_____d (oa/ow)
6. cl_____ (aw/ow)
7. p_____nt (au/ai)
8. b_____n (ir/ur)
9. _____l (ay/ow)
10. th_____sty (oo/ir)
11. yesterd_____ (ai/ay)
12. narr_____ (ow/aw)
13. r_____nd (ow/ou)
14. s_____cer (ou/au)
15. b_____l (oi/oa)

Colour in your score

Test 3

Test 4 le words

There are lots of words that end in **le**.

*a sing**le** eag**le***

thimble	jungle	feeble	handle	purple	
	uncle	angle	needle	circle	simple
article	ladle	grumble	single	steeple	

Write the words that end in ble.

1. _____   2. _____   3. _____

Write the words that end in gle.

4. _____   5. _____   6. _____

Write the words that end in dle.

7. _____   8. _____   9. _____

Write the words that end in ple.

10. _____   11. _____   12. _____

Write the words that end in cle.

13. _____   14. _____   15. _____

Colour in your score

Test 4

Test 5 Punctuation marks

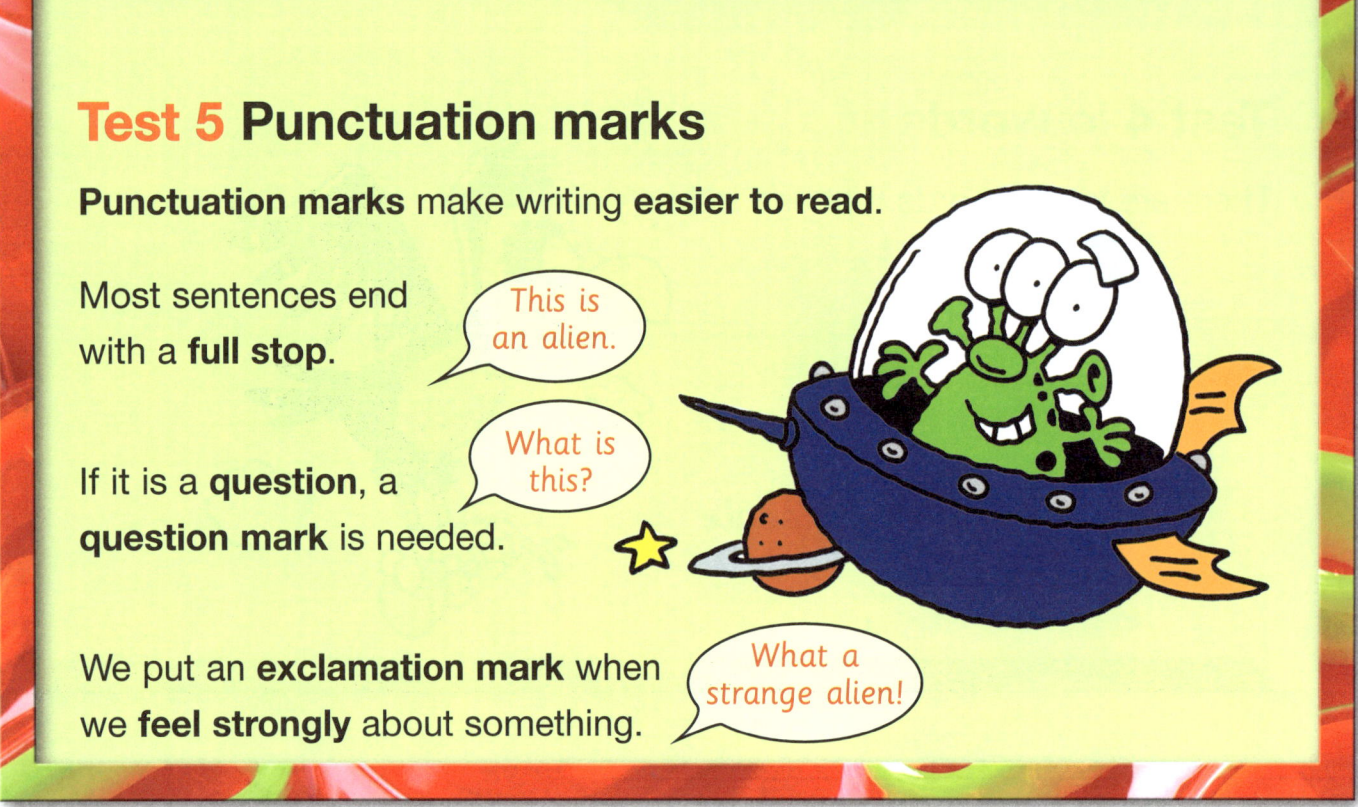

Punctuation marks make writing easier to read.

Most sentences end with a full stop. *This is an alien.*

If it is a question, a question mark is needed. *What is this?*

We put an exclamation mark when we feel strongly about something. *What a strange alien!*

Put in the missing punctuation mark in each sentence.

1. Where do you come from
2. What a funny name
3. The spaceship landed
4. A door opened slowly
5. Run for your life
6. Who is there
7. What do you want
8. It's not fair
9. This is terrible
10. The sun set in the sky
11. The bees buzzed near the flowers
12. How did the car crash
13. When did the letter come
14. Stop that at once
15. We have sausages and chips for tea

Colour in your score

Test 5

Test 6 Speech marks

When we write down what people say we use **speech marks**.

The **words the person says** go **inside** the speech marks.

The lumberjack said, "I cut down trees."

Fill in the missing speech marks.

1. Little Bo Peep said, I've lost my sheep.
2. The mouse said, I ran up the clock.
3. Humpty Dumpty said, I fell off the wall.
4. Incy Wincy Spider said, I climbed up the water spout.
5. Little Jack Horner said, I sat in the corner.
6. I marched up the hill, said the grand old Duke of York.
7. I went to London, said Dick Whittington.
8. I met a wolf, said Little Red Riding Hood.
9. I climbed a beanstalk, said Jack.
10. I ran away, said the gingerbread man.
11. Hansel said, I got lost in a wood.
12. I went to the ball, Cinderella said.
13. Old King Cole said, I'm a merry old soul.
14. I made some tarts, said the Queen of Hearts.
15. I'm very ugly, the troll said.

Colour in your score

Test 6

Test 7 Alphabetical order

Many books are arranged in **alphabetical order**.

anteater **b**ear **c**amel

These words are arranged in alphabetical order according to their **first** letter.

deer **do**g **du**ck

These words are arranged in alphabetical order according to their **second** letter.

Order these words according to their first letter.

1. bat dog cat _____
2. goat elephant fox _____
3. hen kangaroo jaguar _____
4. ostrich monkey lion _____
5. rat seal penguin _____
6. zebra swan panda _____
7. hamster mouse donkey beetle _____
8. ox worm donkey giraffe _____

Order these words according to their second letter.

9. crab cow cat _____
10. bird bull bear _____
11. parrot pike pelican _____
12. shark sardine snake _____
13. trout tiger turtle toad _____
14. giraffe gnu goat gerbil _____
15. bee badger bird buffalo _____

Colour in your score

Test 8 Verbs: past tense

This is happening **now**, so the verb is in the **present tense**.

This happened in the **past**, so the verb is in the **past tense**.

Join up each verb with its past tense.

1. walk — hopped
2. hop — moved
3. carry — copied
4. move — walked
5. arrive — held
6. beg — carried
7. copy — spoke
8. hold — wrote
9. bring — came
10. see — taught
11. speak — arrived
12. take — brought
13. teach — took
14. write — begged
15. come — saw

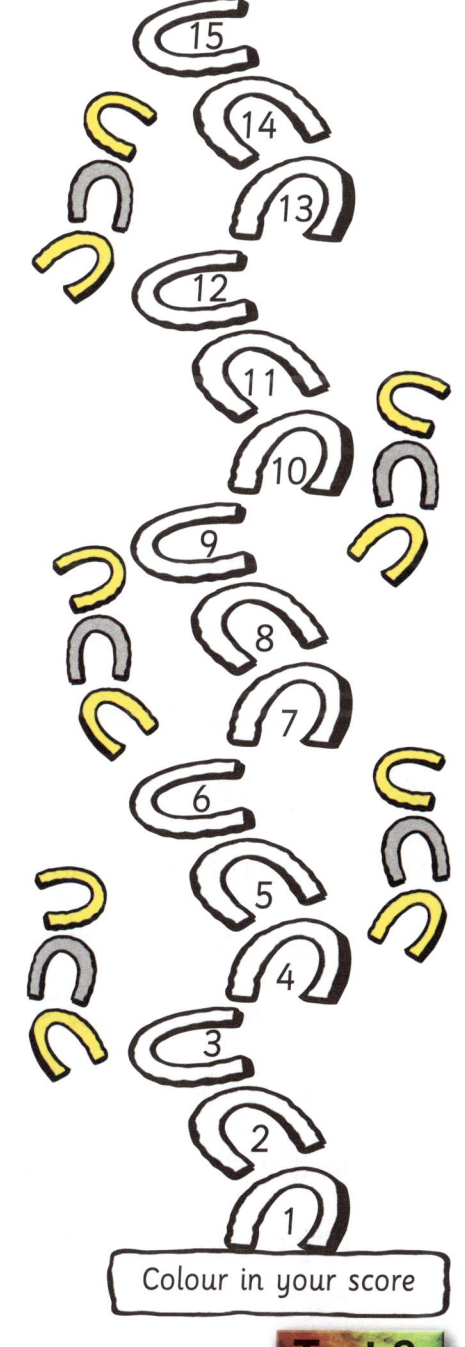

Colour in your score

Test 8

Test 9 Commas

We use **commas** to **separate items in a list**.

We do **not** usually put a comma before the word **and**.

Out of the window I saw a bus, a car, a van and a lorry.

Put in the missing commas in these sentences.

1. My friends are Sam Emma Abdi and Shanaz.
2. March June May and July are months of the year.
3. I like red blue yellow and green.
4. The four seasons are spring summer autumn and winter.
5. I have a dog a cat a fish and a budgie.
6. I hate sprouts cabbage parsnips and leeks.
7. I would like a bike a pen a book and a bag for Christmas.
8. Art science music and maths are good subjects.
9. In my bag I have a pen a ruler a rubber and a book.
10. London Rome Paris and Vienna are all capital cities.
11. I have been to France Spain Greece and Malta.
12. On the farm I saw some cows sheep pigs and hens.
13. On the rock there was a beetle an ant a slug and a snail.
14. In the sky you can see clouds the sun the moon and stars.
15. Crisps chips chocolate and biscuits are not healthy.

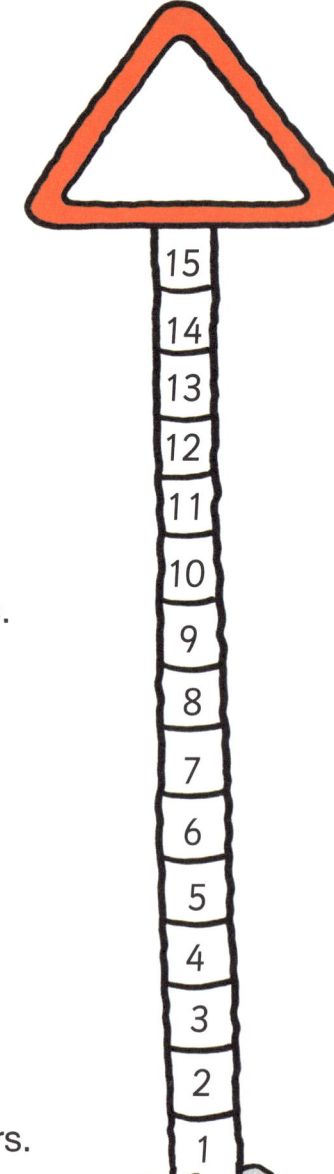

Colour in your score

Test 10 Words inside words

If you look closely, sometimes you can see **small words inside longer words**.

There is an **ape** with a **cap** and a **cape** inside **escape**!

Find a small word 'hiding' in each of these words.

1. father   _____
2. mother   _____
3. heard   _____
4. money   _____
5. know   _____
6. because   _____
7. suddenly   _____
8. friend   _____
9. many   _____
10. wheel   _____
11. stage   _____
12. question   _____
13. narrow   _____
14. rhyme   _____
15. mystery   _____

Colour in your score

Test 10

Test 11 Nouns

A **noun** is a **naming word**. It can be the name of a **person**, **place** or **thing**.

a teacher   a school   a book

Choose the correct noun to complete each sentence.

1. A _____ makes things from wood. (mechanic/carpenter)
2. A _____ makes clothes. (tailor/grocer)
3. A _____ works on a farm. (baker/farmer)
4. A _____ rides horses in races. (diver/jockey)
5. An _____ looks after people's eyes. (doctor/optician)
6. Aeroplanes fly from an _____. (abbey/airport)
7. You can get petrol from a _____. (garden/garage)
8. Ships load and unload at a _____. (dock/church)
9. We keep books in a _____. (lighthouse/library)
10. A _____ is where a king or queen lives. (palace/park)
11. We wash ourselves in a _____. (bed/sink)
12. A _____ is a baby's bed. (cot/cup)
13. Water is boiled in a _____. (knife/kettle)
14. We stir hot drinks with a _____. (spoon/stool)
15. Clothes are kept in a _____. (toaster/wardrobe)

Colour in your score

Test 11

Test 12 Singular and plural

A noun may be **singular** (when there is **only one** thing).

A noun may be **plural** (when there is **more** than one thing).

one bus (singular)

two buses (plural)

Complete these phrases.
Be careful with some of the spellings!

1. one chair, lots of _____
2. one fox, lots of _____
3. one coach, lots of _____
4. one bush, lots of _____
5. one glass, lots of _____
6. one berry, lots of _____
7. one child, lots of _____
8. one man, lots of _____
9. one _____, lots of bikes
10. one _____, lots of boxes
11. one _____, lots of bunches
12. one _____, lots of dishes
13. one _____, lots of copies
14. one _____, lots of lorries
15. one _____, lots of sheep

Colour in your score

Test 12

Test 13 Silent letters

Some words contain **silent letters**.
We cannot hear the letters when we say the words.

com**b**   **k**not

Choose k or w to complete each word.

1. ____rite
2. ____nee
3. ____now
4. ____reck
5. ____rist
6. ____restle
7. ____nock
8. ____night

Choose b or g to complete each word.

9. num____
10. ____nat
11. clim____
12. crum____
13. thum____
14. ____nome
15. ____naw

Colour in your score

Test 14 Adjectives

An **adjective** is a **describing** word. It tells us more about a **noun**.

*a **small** puppy*

Choose the best adjective from the list below to go with each noun.

busy	handsome	dirty	old	beautiful
straight	sharp	heavy	funny	tall
open	muddy	loud	empty	fizzy

1. a _____ weight
2. a _____ ruler
3. a _____ tree
4. a _____ clown
5. a _____ noise
6. a _____ puddle
7. a _____ mark
8. a _____ drink
9. an _____ door
10. a _____ road
11. an _____ glass
12. an _____ ruin
13. a _____ princess
14. a _____ knife
15. a _____ prince

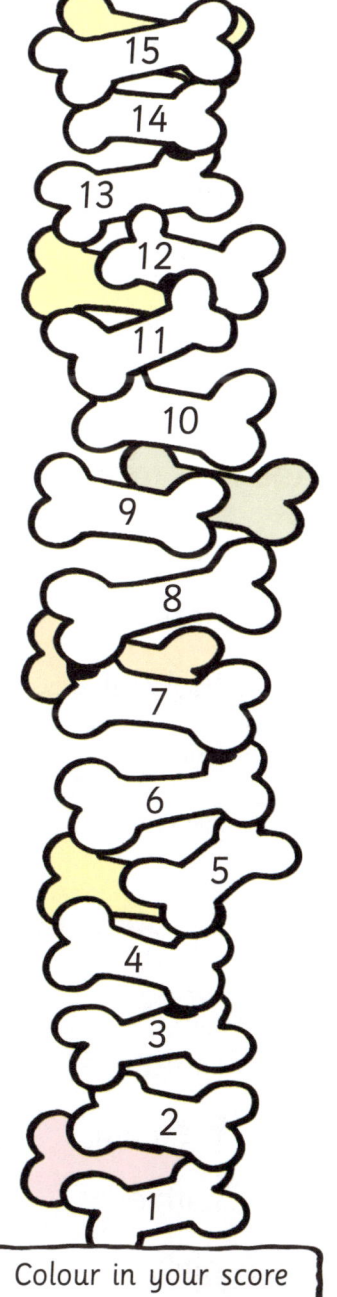

Colour in your score

Test 14

Test 15 Suffixes

A **suffix** is a **group of letters** we add to the **end** of a word.

A suffix changes the **meaning** of the word or the **job** the word does.

power + ful
= powerful

power + less
= powerless

Add ful to the end of each word. Write the words you make.

1. colour   _____
2. pain   _____
3. care   _____
4. thank   _____
5. help   _____

Add less to the end of each word. Write the words you make.

6. use   _____
7. hope   _____
8. thought _____
9. law   _____
10. help   _____

Take the suffix off each word. Write the words you are left with.

11. wonderful _____
12. heartless _____
13. graceful   _____
14. faithless _____
15. pitiful   _____

Colour in your score

Test 15

Test 16 Compound words

A **compound word** is a word made up of **two smaller words**.

hand + bag = handbag

Do these word sums.

1. horse + shoe = _____
2. birth + day = _____
3. foot + step = _____
4. out + side = _____
5. with + out = _____
6. some + one = _____
7. grand + father = _____
8. hair + brush = _____

Write the two words that make up each of these compound words.

9. snowman _____ _____
10. motorway _____ _____
11. toothpaste _____ _____
12. cupboard _____ _____
13. eyesight _____ _____
14. wallpaper _____ _____
15. tablecloth _____ _____

Colour in your score

Test 16

Test 17 Subject and verb agreement

The **subject** (the main person or thing) and the **verb** in each sentence must **agree**.

The birds is flying. ✗   The birds are flying. ✓

Choose the correct form of the verb for each sentence.

1. Bells _____. (ring/rings)
2. The wind _____. (blow/blows)
3. A door _____. (open/opens)
4. Aeroplanes _____. (fly/flies)
5. An owl _____. (hoot/hoots)
6. Chickens _____ eggs. (lay/lays)
7. A rabbit _____ in a burrow. (live/lives)
8. Wolves _____. (howl/howls)
9. Mice _____. (squeak/squeaks)
10. I _____ my dinner. (eat/eats)
11. The children _____ to school. (go/goes)
12. Ben _____ a cold. (have/has)
13. The lady _____ some bread. (buy/buys)
14. Frogs _____. (hop/hops)
15. A cow _____ us milk. (give/gives)

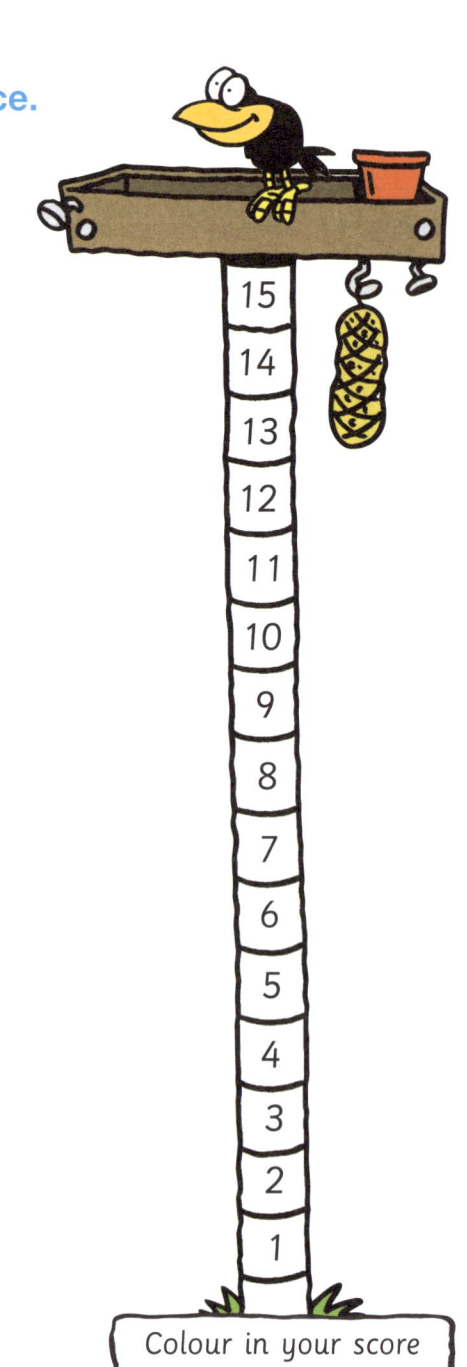

Colour in your score

Test 17

Test 18 Collective nouns

A **collective noun** is the name given to a **group** of things.

a **herd** of cows

bunch   box   library   flock   swarm
chest   shoal   fleet

Choose the best collective noun to complete each phrase.

1. a _____ of matches
2. a _____ of sheep
3. a _____ of bees
4. a _____ of drawers
5. a _____ of ships
6. a _____ of fish
7. a _____ of flowers
8. a _____ of books

sticks   stones   singers   cornflakes
soldiers   trees   bananas

Choose the best word to complete each phrase.

9. a choir of _____
10. an army of _____
11. a packet of _____
12. a forest of _____
13. a bunch of _____
14. a bundle of _____
15. a pile of _____

Colour in your score

Test 18

Test 19 Classifying adjectives

We can classify **adjectives** according to **type**. These adjectives describe **size**.

a **tall** man   a **short** man   a **fat** man

salty	tenth	huge	brown	sour	
tiny	happy	third	green	upset
sweet	yellow	first	annoyed	wide	

Classify the adjectives above.

Colour adjectives

1. _____   2. _____   3. _____

Number adjectives

4. _____   5. _____   6. _____

Adjectives about feelings

7. _____   8. _____   9. _____

Adjectives about taste

10. _____   11. _____   12. _____

Adjectives about size

13. _____   14. _____   15. _____

Colour in your score

Test 19

Test 20 Syllables

When we say a word slowly, we can break it down into **smaller parts**. These parts are called **syllables**. Each syllable must contain at least **one vowel**.

car
(one syllable)

lor + ry
(two syllables)

bull + do + zer
(three syllables)

Say these words slowly. Then write down if they have one, two or three syllables.

1. bus ☐
2. jet ☐
3. ambulance ☐
4. hovercraft ☐
5. ferry ☐
6. drum ☐
7. violin ☐
8. rocket ☐
9. trumpet ☐
10. caravan ☐
11. glider ☐
12. coach ☐
13. aeroplane ☐
14. tractor ☐
15. jeep ☐

Colour in your score

Test 20

Test 21 More prefixes

A **prefix** is a **group of letters** we put in front of a word.
Prefixes **change the meaning** of the word.

behave   misbehave

Choose the prefix re or pre to begin each word.

1. _____turn
2. _____heat
3. _____fix
4. _____pare
5. _____caution
6. _____mind
7. _____fill
8. _____fund

Choose the prefix mis or ex to begin each word.

9. _____judge
10. _____handle
11. _____port
12. _____spell
13. _____lead
14. _____plode
15. _____pand

Colour in your score

Test 22 Pronouns

A **pronoun** is a word that takes the place of a **noun**.

Ben cried when Ben hurt his leg.   Ben cried when **he** hurt his leg.

Choose the best pronoun to complete each sentence.

1. The lady went in the shop. _____ bought some apples. (He/She)
2. _____ am always busy. (We/I)
3. The boy shouted when _____ scored a goal. (he/they)
4. "Why are _____ late?" Mr Shah asked Abdi. (you/he)
5. "_____ are going to the park," the children said. (We/It)
6. _____ is a lovely day. (It/You)
7. Are _____ good at writing? (he/you)
8. _____ like playing games. (We/It)
9. The girl fell off her bike when _____ crashed. (she/you)
10. When the dog stopped _____ barked. (it/they)
11. The prince got up. _____ got dressed. (She/He)
12. I tried to lift the box but _____ was too heavy. (we/it)
13. When I shouted at the birds _____ flew away. (it/they)
14. The boy walked with the girl. _____ went in the park. (We/They)
15. When the man stopped _____ sat down. (you/he)

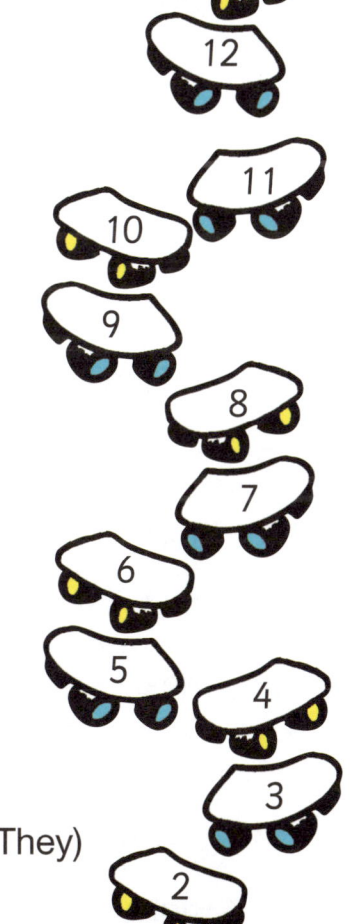

Colour in your score

Test 22

Test 23 Antonyms

Antonyms are words that have the **opposite** meaning.

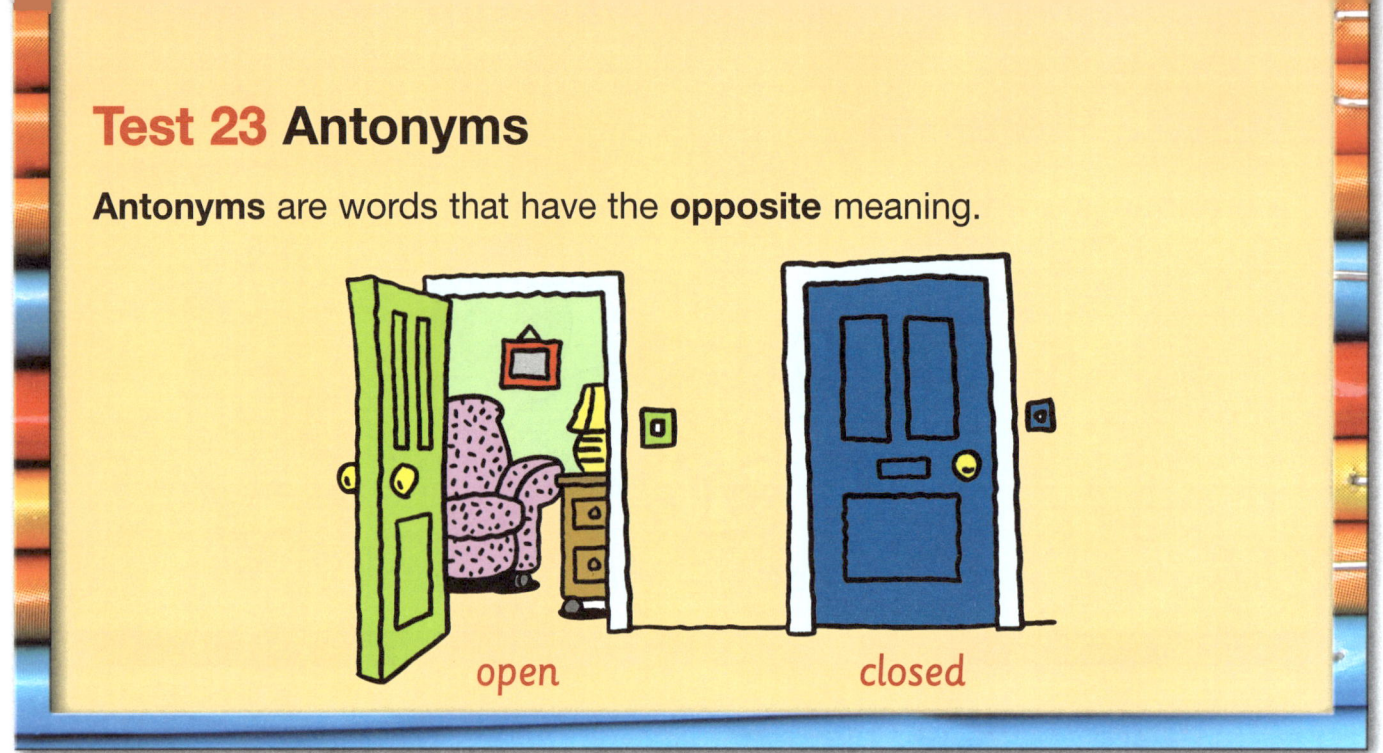

open   closed

Join up the pairs of words with the opposite meaning.

1. wild — white
2. low — hot
3. rough — tame
4. black — bottom
5. cheap — high
6. cold — dear
7. difficult — smooth
8. wide — arrive
9. top — empty
10. first — easy
11. near — left
12. under — far
13. depart — narrow
14. right — over
15. full — last

Colour in your score

Test 23

Test 24 1st and 3rd person

When we are writing about **ourselves** we write in the **first person**. We use pronouns like **I** and **we**.

When we are writing about **others** we write in the **third person**. We use pronouns like **he**, **she**, **it** and **they**.

I called for Ben.
We went swimming.

Annie and Lucy were surprised when **they** opened the box.

Say if each of the pronouns marked in bold is in the first or third person.

1. **I** went to school.
2. Tom went out when **he** finished washing up.
3. The children chattered as **they** ate the bananas.
4. When the dog appeared **it** ran straight home.
5. The flowers looked lovely. **They** were all different colours.
6. **We** went to the cinema in the evening.
7. May **I** have some, please?
8. "**We** can do it!" Tom and Ben shouted.
9. The machine made a loud noise when **it** was turned on.
10. **I** am older than Sam.
11. Mr Shah went to bed. **He** went straight to sleep.
12. The lady was happy but **she** didn't smile.
13. **They** ran for the bus.
14. **I** was too frightened to move.
15. **We** all like to win games.

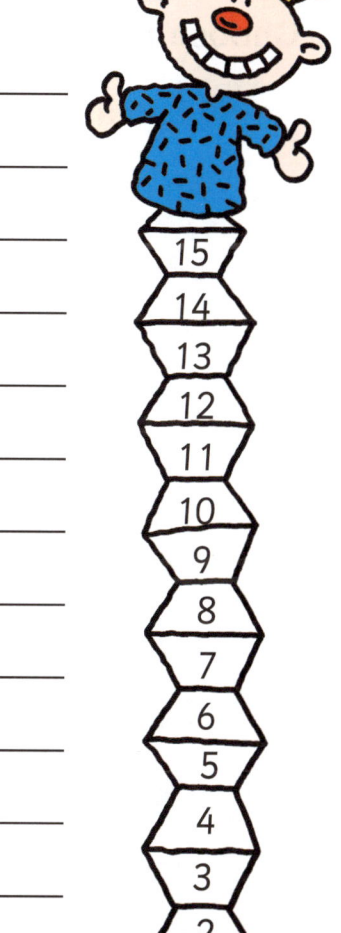

Colour in your score

Test 24

Test 25 Conjunctions

A **conjunction** is a **joining word**. It may be used to join **two sentences**.

I picked up the comic. I read it.   I picked up the comic and read it.

Choose the best conjunction to complete each sentence.

1. I had a bath _____ went to bed. (and/but)
2. An elephant is huge _____ an ant is small. (and/but)
3. I made a sandwich _____ ate it. (and/but)
4. Your towel is wet _____ mine is dry. (and/but)
5. A rabbit is fast _____ a snail is slow. (and/but)
6. I like swimming _____ playing rounders. (and/but)
7. You will get into trouble _____ you talk. (if/so)
8. I was wet _____ it was raining. (if/because)
9. It was hot _____ I took off my jumper. (so/because)
10. The door has been broken _____ I slammed it. (since/when)
11. I ran fast _____ I was late. (if/because)
12. We went for a walk _____ it was very hot. (so/although)
13. I will buy a lolly _____ you give me the money. (if/as)
14. You will get wet _____ you go in the rain. (if/so)
15. My uncle didn't come _____ I didn't see him. (so/if)

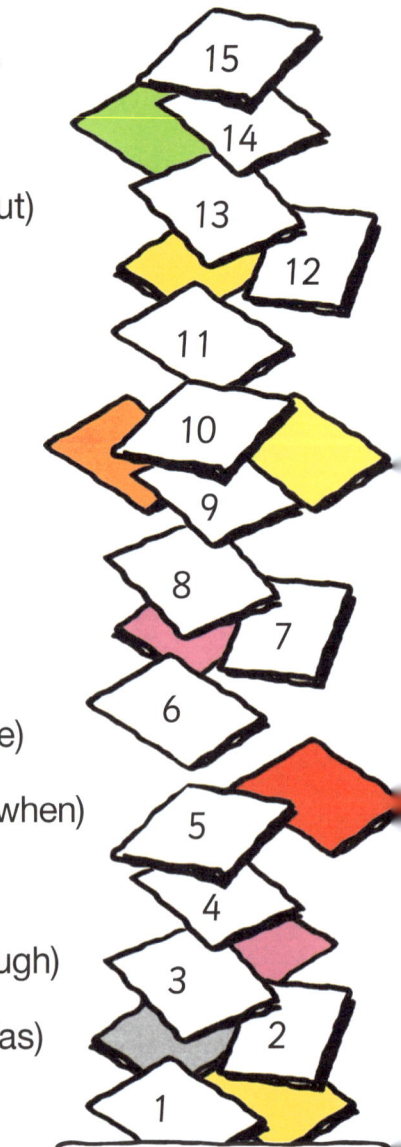

Colour in your score

Test 26 Playing with words

We can make new words by **changing** some letters.

Make some new words.

1. Change the **f** in **f**arm to **ch**. _____
2. Change the **d** in **d**ead to **thr**. _____
3. Change the **w** in **w**ay to **del**. _____
4. Change the **f** in **f**eed to **gr**. _____
5. Change the **n** in **n**erve to **sw**. _____
6. Change the **n** in **n**ew to **scr**. _____
7. Change the **d** in **d**irt to **squ**. _____
8. Change the **m** in **m**oan to **gr**. _____
9. Change the **v** in **v**oice to **ch**. _____
10. Change the **w** in **w**ood to **bl**. _____
11. Change the **l** in **l**oud to **pr**. _____
12. Change the **m** in **m**ow to **borr**. _____
13. Change the **c** in **c**urb to **dist**. _____
14. Change the **d** in **d**are to **bew**. _____
15. Change the **n** in **n**ear to **app**. _____

Colour in your score

Test 26

Test 27 Possessive pronouns

Possessive pronouns tell us who the **owner** of something is.

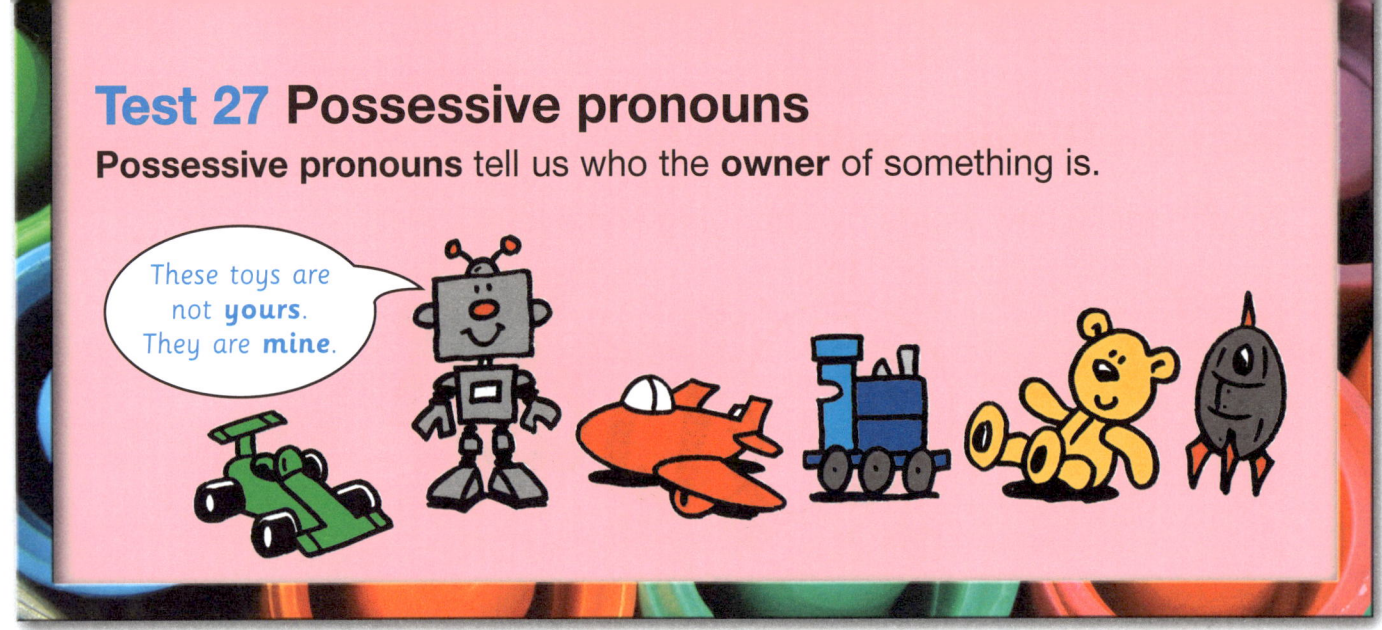

Some common possessive pronouns are:

> mine   yours   his   hers
> its   ours   theirs

<u>Underline</u> the possessive pronoun in each sentence.

1. This book is mine.
2. This bag is blue – yours is red.
3. The boy was sure the pen was his.
4. Sam pointed to Anna and said, "This ruler is hers."
5. Rex belonged to the children – the dog was theirs.
6. "You can't have the ball. It's ours!" Tom and Ben shouted.
7. "The model Ali broke was ours!" Amy and Emma complained.
8. The girl picked up the purse – it was hers.
9. Mr Smith drove a sports car but it was not his.
10. I asked the lady if the pen was hers.
11. Go and look at the bikes. Mine is the silver one.
12. The children said, "These toys are ours!"
13. "I think these smelly socks are yours!" Mum said to John.
14. As soon as Ben won the race, he knew the prize was his!
15. This bag has your name in it so it must be yours.

Colour in your score

Test 27

Test 28 Apostrophes

Sometimes we **shorten** words and leave letters out. These words are called **contractions**. We use an **apostrophe** to show where letters are missing.

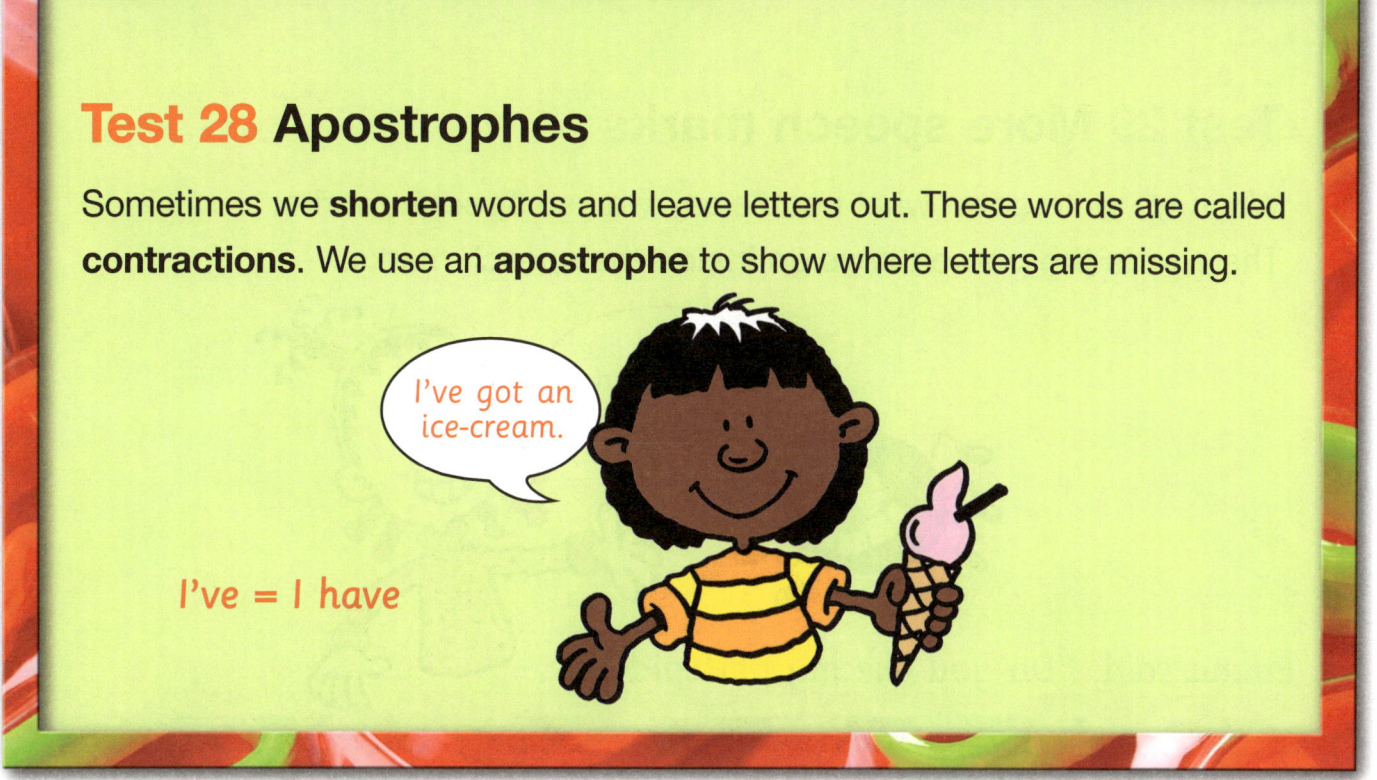

I've = I have

Put in the missing apostrophes in the correct places in these contractions.

1. I m
2. h e s
3. I v e
4. w e d
5. I l l
6. w o u l d n t
7. w e r e
8. h e r e s
9. d o e s n t
10. i t s
11. w a s n t
12. w h o s
13. w o n t
14. d o n t
15. y o u r e

Colour in your score

Test 28

Test 29 More speech marks

When we write down what people say we use **speech marks**.
The **words the person says** go **inside** the speech marks.

Emma said, "Do you like my pet spider?"

Put in the missing speech marks in these sentences.

1. Hello, Ben said.
2. It's nice to see you, Sam replied.
3. What a lovely day! exclaimed Ben.
4. Yes, it's so warm, Sam answered.
5. The weather forecast said it would rain, Ben said.
6. I don't think it will, Sam replied.
7. I can see a few black clouds, Ben commented.
8. I think they will pass over, Sam said.
9. Where are you off to? Ben asked.
10. I'm going to town to do some shopping, Sam answered.
11. May I come? Ben asked.
12. Yes, of course. Shall we walk or wait for a bus? Sam said.
13. Let's walk, Ben suggested.
14. I think I can feel a few spots of rain, Sam said.
15. Let's get the bus, then, said Ben.

Colour in your score

Test 30 Proper nouns

A **proper noun** is a **special** (or **particular**) name of a **person**, **place** or **thing**. Proper nouns always begin with a **capital letter**.

Here is **W**ayne.   **N**ew **Y**ork is in **A**merica.   This is the **E**mpire **S**tate **B**uilding.

Rewrite these proper nouns correctly.

1. anna   _____
2. mr khan   _____
3. doctor parker   _____
4. bert   _____
5. washington   _____
6. green park   _____
7. high street   _____
8. charing cross station   _____
9. daily mirror   _____
10. tottenham hotspur   _____
11. wednesday   _____
12. february   _____
13. christmas   _____
14. golden sands hotel   _____
15. moscow   _____

Colour in your score

Test 30

ANSWERS

Test 1
The missing prefix is in **bold**.
1. **un**pack
2. **un**well
3. **dis**place
4. **dis**trust
5. **un**fair
6. **un**happy
7. **dis**agree
8. **dis**may
9. **un**load
10. **un**bolt
11. **dis**honest
12. **un**do
13. **dis**arm
14. **dis**charge
15. **dis**please

Test 2
1. disappeared
2. spoke
3. chased
4. brushed
5. painted
6. knocking
7. drinking
8. groaned
9. pushing
10. shining
11. roared
12. crashed
13. flapped
14. hopped
15. came

Test 3
The correct phoneme is in **bold**.
1. m**oo**n
2. tr**ea**t
3. gr**ow**
4. gl**ue**
5. r**oa**d
6. cl**aw**
7. p**ai**nt
8. b**ur**n
9. **ow**l
10. thir**s**ty
11. yesterd**ay**
12. narr**ow**
13. r**ou**nd
14. s**au**cer
15. b**oi**l

Test 4
1. thimble
2. feeble
3. grumble
4. jungle
5. angle
6. single
7. handle
8. needle
9. ladle
10. purple
11. simple
12. steeple
13. uncle
14. circle
15. article

Test 5
1. Where do you come from?
2. What a funny name!
3. The spaceship landed.
4. A door opened slowly.
5. Run for your life!
6. Who is there?
7. What do you want?
8. It's not fair!
9. This is terrible!
10. The sun set in the sky.
11. The bees buzzed near the flowers.
12. How did the car crash?
13. When did the letter come?
14. Stop that at once!
15. We have sausages and chips for tea.

Test 6
1. Little Bo Peep said, "I've lost my sheep."
2. The mouse said, "I ran up the clock."
3. Humpty Dumpty said, "I fell off the wall."
4. Incy Wincy Spider said, "I climbed up the water spout."
5. Little Jack Horner said, "I sat in the corner."
6. "I marched up the hill," said the grand old Duke of York.
7. "I went to London," said Dick Whittington.
8. "I met a wolf," said Little Red Riding Hood.
9. "I climbed a beanstalk," said Jack.
10. "I ran away," said the gingerbread man.
11. Hansel said, "I got lost in a wood."
12. "I went to the ball," Cinderella said.
13. Old King Cole said, "I'm a merry old soul."
14. "I made some tarts," said the Queen of Hearts.
15. "I'm very ugly," the troll said.

Test 7
1. bat   cat   dog
2. elephant   fox   goat
3. hen   jaguar   kangaroo
4. lion   monkey   ostrich
5. penguin   rat   seal
6. panda   swan   zebra
7. beetle   donkey   hamster   mouse
8. donkey   giraffe   ox   worm
9. cat   cow   crab
10. bear   bird   bull
11. parrot   pelican   pike
12. sardine   shark   snake
13. tiger   toad   trout   turtle
14. gerbil   giraffe   gnu   goat
15. badger   bee   bird   buffalo

Test 8
1. walked
2. hopped
3. carried
4. moved
5. arrived
6. begged
7. copied
8. held
9. brought
10. saw
11. spoke
12. took
13. taught
14. wrote
15. came

Test 9
1. My friends are Sam, Emma, Abdi and Shanaz.
2. March, June, May and July are months of the year.
3. I like red, blue, yellow and green.
4. The four seasons are spring, summer, autumn and winter.
5. I have a dog, a cat, a fish and a budgie.
6. I hate sprouts, cabbage, parsnips and leeks.
7. I would like a bike, a pen, a book and a bag for Christmas.
8. Art, science, music and maths are good subjects.
9. In my bag I have a pen, a ruler, a rubber and a book.
10. London, Rome, Paris and Vienna are all capital cities.
11. I have been to France, Spain, Greece and Malta.
12. On the farm I saw some cows, sheep, pigs and hens.
13. On the rock there was a beetle, an ant, a slug and a snail.
14. In the sky you may see clouds, the sun, the moon and stars.
15. Crisps, chips, chocolate and biscuits are not healthy.

Test 10
1. fat (or) her (or) the
2. the (or) moth (or) her
3. ear (or) hear
4. one (or) on
5. now (or) no
6. use (or) be (or) cause (or) us
7. den
8. end
9. man (or) any (or) an
10. eel (or) heel
11. tag (or) age (or) stag
12. quest (or) on
13. row (or) arrow
14. me
15. my

Test 11
1. carpenter
2. tailor
3. farmer
4. jockey
5. optician
6. airport
7. garage
8. dock
9. library
10. palace
11. sink
12. cot
13. kettle
14. spoon
15. wardrobe

Test 12
1. chairs
2. foxes
3. coaches
4. bushes
5. glasses
6. berries
7. children
8. men
9. bike
10. box
11. bunch
12. dish
13. copy
14. lorry
15. sheep